The Rock Pool SOS

Written by
Polly Walker
and illustrated by
Helen Braid

For Elodee and Paige,
with all my love, Mummy xx

Published by:

Small World, Big Imaginations Ltd

www.smlworld.co.uk

ISBN: 978-1-910966-36-5

Printed in the United Kingdom.

The Rockpool SOS by Polly Walker

This children's book aims to encourage thinking about how to overcome peer disagreements and develop respectful relationships, through collaborative problem solving, positive communication and active listening. A number of suggested fun and empowering talking points and activities are included towards the back which can be used informally in the home, or adapted to fit various areas of the primary curriculum – in particular to complement the Social and Emotional Aspects of Learning units – 'Getting on and Falling Out' and 'Relationships', as well as PSHE and literacy.

'Polly has written a lovely book for younger children which will help them to engage with important words and ideas around conflict and related feelings. I'm sure it will provide a useful complement to schools seeking to support effective peer mediation as part of their PSHE curriculum'.

Chris Seaton
CEO of Schoolsworks Academy Trust and Director of Peaceworks

'This delightful book illustrates how easy it is to get into a conflict when we jump to conclusions, think only about ourselves and fail to really listen to each other. It also shows how a simple set of strategies can help us find 'win-win' ways forward that address everyone's needs. The ideas are clear and easy to understand, and the illustrations help to make them even more memorable. Who would have imagined that a small rock pool could contain such drama - and also such wisdom!
The Teachers' Notes provide lots of suggestions to make even more of this deceptively simple tale.'

Belinda Hopkins
Transforming Conflict

Ten **happy** sea creatures

In a small rock pool

Calm waters, smiley faces

Everything is cool

Ten **worried** sea creatures
Hear of storms ahead

Together they prepare,
Filled with **fear** and **dread**.

Ten **bold** sea creatures

Together they are **brave!**

They face **furious** waters

Wave after gigantic wave!

Ten curious sea creatures
The storm delivered a shell.
It is beautiful and mysterious

But it casts an evil spell...

Ten divided sea creatures

Hiding out of sight.

Two are cross,

eight feel sad.

How can they end this fight?

The swirling stormy waters clear

Revealing a Wise Old Whelk

He comes in peace and he brings,

Calming words to heal and help.

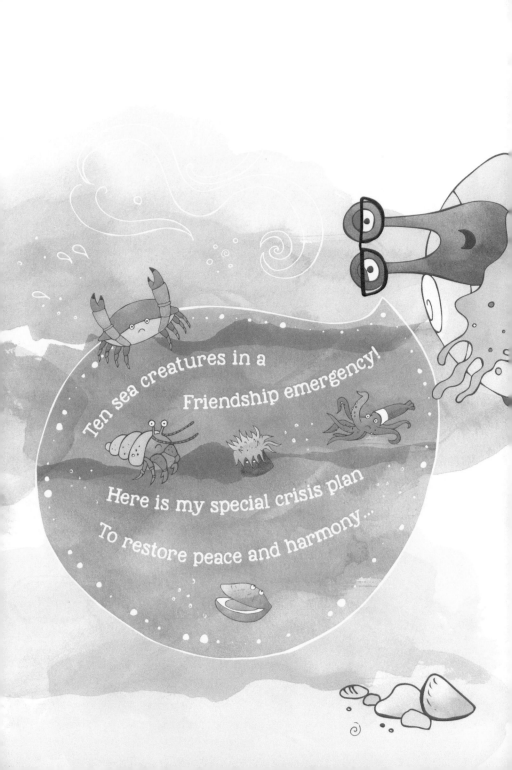

Ten sea creatures in a
Friendship emergency!

Here is my special crisis plan

To restore peace and harmony...

Use **truthful** words to build bridges
        not to hurt or burn,
Calm voices to tell your story - when
Ears to listen, don't interrupt - eve
Use your brains together - solv
Ask others to assist, if yo
But! They must b
And never, eve

your turn.

you disagree.

blems creatively.

d a helpful guide.

m and fair,

ke sides.

Ten determined sea creatures
Meet together in the coral.

They talk and listen and share ideas,
Working hard to solve their quarrel.

And before too long,

An interesting discovery is made.

Inside the shell was a pearl

And crab wanted it for his cave.

"I didn't want the pearl!"

Excitedly shrimp said.

"The shell itself is what I want

To make a cosy bed!"

Two **calm** and **cheerful** sea creatures
Were BOTH **happy** in the end.

And eight more sea creatures

Were glad to help their friends.

Ten **cheerful** sea creatures
Together living peacefully
And now they know what to do

When they don't agree.

Teacher/Parent Discussion Ideas & Activities

Schools - All activities can be adapted to suit different age groups and to compliment the work carried out in *SEAL: Getting on and Falling Out* and also *Relationships*. There are many other cross-curricular links - literacy / Religious Education / Citizenship / Art etc.

Words

1. Most pages in the story mention how the sea creatures are feeling:

E.g. 'Ten happy sea creatures'

Can you find other words in the book that describe how the creatures are feeling? How do their feelings change throughout the book? Why do you think this is?

2. There are some words used in the story to describe how the creatures behaved when Shrimp and Crab started fighting: snaps, zaps, etc. Can you find any more? What do you think it would have been like to be in the rock pool at this time? Now turn to the end of the story. What would it have been like to be in the rock pool now? Can you think of some words to describe how the creatures might have been feeling at the end of the story and what the atmosphere would have been like in the rock pool?

3. The Wise Old Whelk suggests using words to *'build bridges not to hurt or burn'*. What do you think this means? When might words be used as bridges? How can words hurt or burn? What did Shrimp and Crab say to each other that may have hurt the other? Look at the argument that took place between Shrimp and Crab. How could Crab and Shrimp have communicated what they wanted in a kinder way so that they could say what they wanted without hurting the other's feelings?

4. Do you think that the way that you say words can alter the way they are understood? Experiment with saying words in a calm manner or an angry way and think about how the tone of your voice can change the meaning of what you are saying. For example: CACTUS is a sharp, snappy word. Can you make it sound calming? RHUBARB rolls off the tongue, but can you make it sound angry?

Feelings

1. Can you think of some examples of different feelings? How might other people's behaviour, actions, or words change how you are feeling?

2. In the story, the creatures were feeling 'cross and sad' and all went into their homes to hide away whilst Shrimp and Crab were quarrelling. Why do you think they did this?

3. What do you do when you are feeling sad or angry? Perhaps you could think of some things that you can do to help when you're feeling sad. Here are some ideas to get you started:

*I can find a nice quiet area and do a calm activity that I enjoy -
read a good book, do some drawing etc.*

I can find an adult that I trust and talk to them about what is worrying me.

I go outside and listen to the birds and enjoy the nature around me - I look at the patterns on the leaves and the colourful flowers, I watch the interesting clouds gliding by. All of these things help me to calm down and feel better.

4. Imagine a 'toolbox for your mind' and in the toolbox are all the things that you need to help if you're feeling sad. What would you put in your toolbox? Here are some ideas of what I would include in my own toolbox - *spending time with my friends and family, walks in the countryside, the warm sunshine, spending time reading a really good book, a nice cup of tea...*

Friendships

1. The Wise Old Whelk talks about friendships being tricky and that occasionally they can go wrong. What do you think could make a friendship go wrong? What do you and your friends do if you disagree about something? What do you think makes a good friend? Is it important to spend your time with people that you feel good around, that you can have fun with and be yourself with? Think about your closest friends - what is special about them? How do they make you feel?

2. When somebody is unexpectedly really kind to you, it can really make your day! Perhaps somebody stopped to help you when you dropped your things in the street? Or somebody came to play with you on the playground when you were all alone? Can you think of when somebody was kind to you and it made you happy? Now can you think of some ways to be kind and make others really happy when they are not expecting it? Maybe try this: In your class, think of somebody that you don't usually play with. Now think of something really great about that person - Perhaps they're good at maths? Perhaps they're very creative? Maybe they find the best places to hide in Hide and Seek? Why don't you tell them and see how happy it makes them?

3. The creatures in the rock pool were all affected when Crab and Shrimp fell out. If somebody in your class, your family, or your friendship group falls out, how does it make you feel?

Resolving Conflict

1. *(A role-play activity)* Two volunteers are required who are happy to act out this story in role (this is a great activity for adults to act out for children, perhaps in assembly). The participants are given an orange between them.

Participant 1 - must be told secretly that they just want the juice from the orange to drink

Participant 2 - must be told secretly that they just want the peel from the orange for a cake recipe

The participants act out a quarrel in which both believe that they should have the orange, without divulging why.

The audience must then give their input through careful questioning to assist the volunteers in resolving their dispute - Why do you feel that you should have the orange? What do you need it for? Until it can be established that both parties can leave with what they wanted. What is the message of the activity? And the book?

2. Explore what the word *compromise* means. Have you ever been in a situation where you have shared or compromised - maybe you and a friend both wanted the same thing? What happened? Were you both happy in the end?

3. This is an activity to highlight how we can all view the same object or issue very differently, without our individual views necessarily being wrong. Using a chunk of triangular cheese, discuss how it looks depending on which way you are viewing it - triangular from above, rectangular from the end etc. Talk about what you have found out. Is it right that even when we don't agree we should still try to respect one another's views? If working with older children, you could start to explore how situations like this can escalate into much more serious situations around the world.

4. The Wise Old Whelk gave the creatures some advice about how to solve their quarrels. Why do you think that it is important -

To tell the truth?

To take it in turns and use calm voices?

To listen to what the other person has to say even if you don't agree with them?

To solve your problems together?

5. Why would you ask somebody not involved in the argument to help solve it? Why must they not take sides? Is there anybody in your class or your school that you can ask to help - maybe you have a peer mediator?

6. Can you write your own special crisis plan for when you or your friends have a falling out? You could include some of your calming down activities or ideas from your toolbox.

7. Perhaps you could write your own story / cartoon / storyboard showing how a conflict came about and how it was resolved. Maybe you could even act out your story using puppets!